Campfire Funnies

ISBN 0-439-81738-2

12 11 10 9 8 7 6 5 4 3 2 1   6 7 8 9 10 11/0

Printed in the U.S.A.

First Scholastic printing, January 2006

Campfire Funnies

by David Lewman

SCHOLASTIC INC.

New York Toronto London Auckland Sydney
Mexico City New Delhi Hong Kong Buenos Aires

What does SpongeBob sleep on
when he goes camping?

A square mattress.

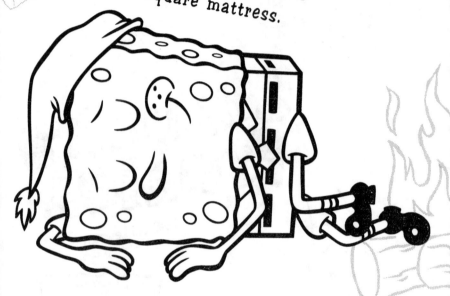

Why did Plankton smash all
the tents?

Because he wanted to
break camp.

Sandy: What do sheep carry their tents in?

SpongeBob: *Baaaaaackpacks.*

Squidward: What do you get when you cross a bag with an elephant?

Sandy: A backpachyderm.

5

SpongeBob: Why don't tents have any money?

Mr. Krabs: They're always being held up.

Where does Mr. Krabs keep the sticks that hold up his tent?

In a pole vault.

Mr. Krabs: Why will you never go hungry in a tent?

Patrick: Because you'll always have plenty of stakes.

7

SpongeBob: What kind of fire is best for cleaning?

Plankton: A brush fire.

Plankton: Why did the gambler pull up the tent pegs?

Plankton's Computer Wife, Karen: He wanted to raise the stakes.

How did Bubble Buddy like the camping trip?

He was blown away.

Squidward: Was the log entertaining at the wienie roast?

Patrick: Yes, he was on fire.

Why did Patrick throw the candy on the burning log?

He wanted to make a bonbon fire.

Patrick: What do you use to fix a broken fire?

Sandy: A fire drill.

Mr. Krabs: What did the big tent say to the noisy little tent?

Plankton: "Zip it!"

Squidward: What's the secret to opening a tent door?

SpongeBob: You have to know the zip code.

Why is Patrick on a hike like a campfire in the rain?

They're both hard to start.

SpongeBob: What should you carry at night when you're camping underwater?

Sandy: Your splashlight.

Sandy: What did the big camping lantern say to the dark little lantern?

SpongeBob: "Lighten up!"

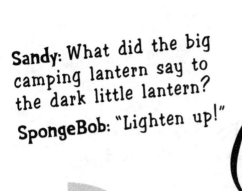

What does Mr. Krabs carry at night when he's camping?

His cashlight.

SpongeBob: How can you tell when a campfire's sick?

Mrs. Puff: When it doesn't feel so hot.

Mrs. Puff: How did the branch avoid the campfire?

Patrick: He took a stick day.

Sandy: What did the tent think of the campground?

SpongeBob: It was love at first site.

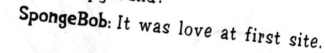

Sandy: Why are lightning bugs always on time?

SpongeBob: Because they're always there in a flash.

Sandy: Did the tent stake have a good date with the rope?

Mr. Krabs: Yes, they decided to tie the knot.

SpongeBob: How did you know Patrick's canteen had a hole in it?

Sandy: It just leaked out.

Patrick: What kind of match is no good for starting a campfire?

SpongeBob: A tennis match.

Squidward: What happened to the log that wouldn't burn?

Plankton: He finally met his match.

SpongeBob: What kind of book has no title, no chapters, and no pages?

Sandy: A matchbook.

What happened when SpongeBob left his library book outside the tent overnight?

In the morning it was over-dew.

What happened to SpongeBob's idea for a flying tent?

It never got off the ground.

Squidward: Why did the woodchuck take all the campsites?

Sandy: He was a groundhog.

What does Patrick make by the campfire late at night?

S'nores.

Why did Gary keep sliding out of his tent?

He was on his slipping bag.

Where does Patrick eat soup when he goes camping?

In his slurping bag.

Why did Patrick stick warm bread in his sleeping bag?

So his sleeping bag would be nice and toasty.

Squidward: Are hot dogs brave?

Plankton: No, they're wienies.

Squidward: Was the camper mad at his tent when it leaked?

SpongeBob: No, they patched things up.

Why does SpongeBob never take more than two hikes in one day?

Because three hikes and you're out.

Why didn't SpongeBob want to talk about his feet after the hike?

They were a sore subject.

What did Patrick find when he dug under his tent?

He struck soil.

SpongeBob: What's the worst kind of weather for a long hike?

Squidward: Blistery.

Why is it so hard for Patrick to sleep if there's a rock under him?

He's used to having the rock *over* him!

Why did Patrick pitch his tent on a boulder?

He wanted to be the new kid on the rock.

SpongeBob: Which campsites are the shiniest?

Patrick: The ones with aluminum soil.

What's SpongeBob's favorite national park?

Yellowstone.

SpongeBob: Is the ground easy to sleep on?

Squidward: No, it's hard.

SpongeBob: What do starfish like to do around a campfire?

Patrick: Have a cling-along.

What kind of camping food does Plankton make at the Chum Bucket?

Beef spew.

SpongeBob: What do jellyfish like to do around a campfire?

Squidward: Have a sting-along.

SpongeBob: Why did the chicken cross the campground?

Patrick: To get to the other site.

Sandy: Why did the fish study camping?

Mrs. Puff: She wanted to join the Girl Trouts.

Patrick: Why did the camper sleep with her head in the grass?

SpongeBob: She wanted to wake up with a new hair dew.

Sandy: What's the difference between the shoes you wear to go camping and two owls on a bicycle?

Squidward: One's a pair of hiking boots and the other's a pair of biking hoots.

SpongeBob: How did the doctor invent a cure for poison ivy?

Sandy: He started from scratch.

Why did Patrick hike through the poison ivy?

He was itching to go.

Why did the bug dig below the tent Patrick's family was in?

He wanted to sleep under the Stars.

Plankton: Who helps campers and keeps the trees in order?

Squidward: The forest arranger.

SpongeBob: Why did the tent agree to stand up all night?
Squidward: He was roped into it.

Plankton: What kind of knot should you never use on a tent rope?

Mrs. Puff: An astronaut.

Squidward: What is the rope expert's motto?

Mr. Krabs: "If at first you don't succeed, tie, tie again."

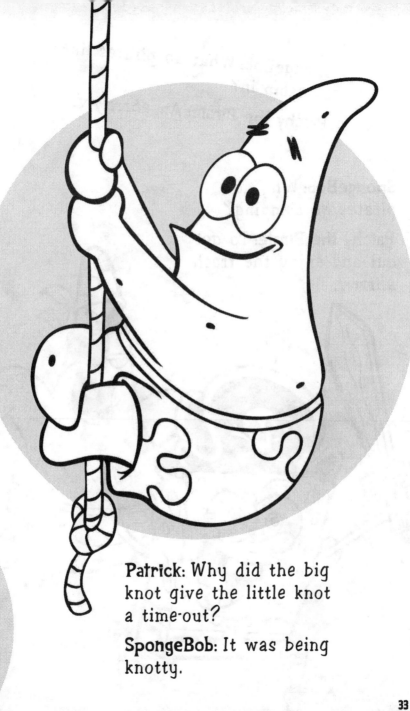

Patrick: Why did the big knot give the little knot a time-out?

SpongeBob: It was being knotty.

SpongeBob: What do pirates like to camp in?

Patchy the Pirate: An *ahrrrrr-v*.

SpongeBob: Why do pirates go camping?

Patchy the Pirate: To get out and enjoy the fresh *ahrrrrr*.

Plankton: What kind of cot is the worst to sleep on?

Squidward: An apricot.

Sandy: What's huge, lives in a lake, and never remembers to bring a compass?

Squidward: The Lost Ness Monster.

What does Sandy always remember to take when she goes hiking?

Her furs aid kit.

Why did Patrick punch the dirt path?

He heard it was time to hit the trail.

What does the Flying Dutchman sleep on when he goes camping?

A scare mattress.

Sandy: What should you remember to take with you when you hike through the Fairy-Tale Woods?

SpongeBob: An up-to-date troll guide.

SpongeBob: Where did the sloppy camper go hiking?

Sandy: The wildermess.

Squidward: Where did the clumsy camper go hiking?

Plankton: The great ouchdoors.

Patrick: What has long fangs, wears a big cape, and sleeps all day in a tent?
Squidward: A campire.

Why did Patrick tie a leash to the tent?

He heard it was a pup tent.

Pearl: What part of the tent did Cinderella break?

Mrs. Puff: The glass zipper.

Pearl: Why are some musicians especially good at putting up tents?

Squidward: Because they have perfect pitch.

39

Plankton: What kind of stick makes the worst kindling?

Pearl: Lipstick.

Squidward: What kind of branch never burns?

Sandy: The branch of a river.

If Squidward were a branch, what kind would he be?

A stick-in-the-mud.

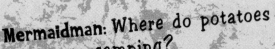
Mermaidman: Where do potatoes like to go camping?

Barnacleboy: In a mashional park.

Mermaidman: Why did the old camper make the young camper crawl around his tent?

Barnacleboy: He wanted to show him the ropes.

What's Mrs. Puff's favorite campfire activity?

Testing marshmallows.

Mr. Krabs: Why are campers never satisfied?

Plankton: Because they always want s'mores.

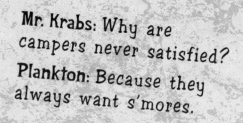

SpongeBob: What do cows like to make over a campfire?

Sandy: S'moo-rs.

What did SpongeBob tell Patrick when he was searching for the campfire?

"You're getting warmer!"

Why did Patrick just pretend to go on the trail?

He thought Squidward told him to fake a hike.

Squidward: Why did the robbers go camping?

Plankton: They wanted to go on a nice, long heist.

Why did Patrick pitch his tent between a state park and a national park?

He'd always wanted to double-park.

What's the difference between the Patty Wagon and a hiker?

One's got two front seats and the other's got two sore feet.

Patrick: What's every mosquito's favorite bedtime story?

SpongeBob: *Snow Bite and the Seven Pores.*

How did Patrick choose which hot dog to roast?

"Wienie, meeny, miny, mo . . ."

Mr. Krabs: What kind of fire makes the worst campfire?

Squidward: A sapphire.

How does Plankton's computer wife start her day when she's camping?

She boots up.

GOOD NiGHT.